THE MA

Sharon Telfer grew up on Teesside and now lives in East Yorkshire, where she works as a freelance editor. She has won the Reflex Flash Fiction Prize and, twice, the Bath Flash Fiction Award. Her work appears in *Best Small Fictions* 2021. She was awarded the New Writing North/Word Factory Northern Short Story Apprenticeship in 2018. In 2020, she placed second in the Bath Short Story Award. Her work has been selected for *Test Signal*, an anthology of the best contemporary Northern writing, published by Dead Ink Books and Bloomsbury in 2021. She is a founding editor at *FlashBack Fiction*, an online lit mag showcasing historical flash fiction.

The Map Waits

Sharon Telfer

REFLEX PRESS

First published as a collection in 2021 by Reflex Press
Abingdon, Oxfordshire, OX14 3SY
www.reflex.press

A CIP catalogue record of this book is
available from the British Library.

ISBN: 978-1-914114-00-7

1 3 5 7 9 10 8 6 4 2

Printed and bound in Great Britain by
Imprint Digital, Upton Pyne, Exeter

Cover image by Vera Petruk/Shutterstock.com

www.reflex.press/the-map-waits/

For Mum, who brought me Milly-Molly-Mandy and
Pookie the Flying Rabbit from Fairfield Library,
and Dad, who read me Num-Num and Bunny Cuddles
(he loves his jam!)

CONTENTS

Telegraph

First came men with stakes and measures, next the hole-diggers, then the pole-setters, last of all the wire party. Ox-wagons, heavy with felled trees, shook the dust from the earth.

The workers had such a thirst she feared they'd drain the well. Her silent husband counted the bills they paid him into the strongbox under the bed.

A young Irishman showed her the tiny machine at the head of the line. It clicked like a locust, devouring words.

They rumbled onward, straight, across the plains. She shaded her eyes 'til all she could see of them was a dot. Her husband flattened her, then, for talking to the Irishman.

Now, while he harrows the fields, she leans against the pole, one hand on her swelling belly. She listens to the wind humming through the wire, imagines the words chattering up and down, the swarms of unseen people in cities faraway.

First Catch Your Hare

Michael sees the skin first, hung up like a lost glove. Then the body, red as hawthorn berries. The cat sits watching the blood drip with its peat-pool eyes.

Mammy smacks his head for lateness, sends him back out for herbs to stew with the hare his brother has caught.

There is a hollow in the herb patch where Michael had seen it lying, ears flat, as he stole past at dawn. Tracing the curve, his hand lifts the sharp scent of vervain. He rubs his bruised lip and thinks of what he and Fintan have done.

~

He passes Fintan at the communion rail. Their eyes do not meet. Kneeling, Michael can smell vervain on his fingers. As the chalice presses his lip, Michael winces. Above, Christ hangs, suspended in glass.

Outside, Donal O'Casey catches Michael's brother by the arm. Their heads draw close, turn back towards him.

~

Mammy serves the broth first, then says grace. A sharp pain flicks Michael's eyes open. It is the cat, its claws in his thigh. Across the table, his brother's stare is fixed upon him.

His first spoonful stings with salt, the second is a grassy burst of vervain, the third rich with iron blood. Michael's ears fill with the remembered tug and hush of the waves; he feels again Fintan's mouth, rough and sweet on his. He wishes himself away from the dark kitchen, back with his love on the tide-washed sand.

The cat spikes, hisses. Spoons stopped, mouths gaping, they see the hare rise from the pot, pull on its pelt, dash into the midsummer evening with a shake of golden fur. A chair crashes to the floor as Michael follows, leaping across the peat, racing westward to the shore, towards the glittering sea.

A Jolly Good Fellow

They line us all up in the schoolyard. Me and Billy too, though we've work in the fields with summer come early and everything ripe before it should.

Ma'd scraped Evie's hair into pigtails. 'Stop your fussing, Evangeline Carter,' she said. 'Don't you want to look pretty for Mr Pritchard's fare-thee-well?' Evie just stood shaking her head while Ma tried to fix the ribbons, 'til Ma give her a clip. Last harvest, you could no more hush Evie's prattle than you could stop a lark's beak. She don't say much, though, these days.

All on us, in us Sunday best, holding them little flags from the day they crowned the new King. Vicar says summat, how sad Mr Pritchard is going away so sudden, like. Mr Pritchard, he goes red in the sun while we sing 'For He's a Jolly Good Fellow' and waves us flags and all the grown-ups join in.

Along the line he come, shaking each on us by the hand. Folks is always saying, how he's such a fine schoolmaster, taught us such nice manners. But when he comes to me and Evie, Evie hides behind my legs, like she's shy.

I grip his hand firm, though it's smooth and slippy with sweat. I look at him square, man to man, like. And I say the words real careful, just how I've said each one in my head stooping over the corn, 'Godspeed to the city, sir. You will never want to come back to our little village, I am sure.' Sun's in his eyes, maybe, leastways he keeps 'em down, cheeks blazing like poppies.

And Evie slips her fingers into mine, and I squeeze 'em soft back, as Mr Pritchard pulls his hand away and goes off down the line.

Terra Incognita

The galleys wallow home, bellies low with other men's gold. The sailors stagger to the brothels. The masters go first to banker, barber, court, then to the mapmaker.

On lookout, she spies them, stumbling over cobbles, ducking the jutting houses.

She whispers each name so her father can greet them. They sit heavily, still unsteady on the unmoving land. She brings soft cheese, cherries, peaches – whatever is ripe.

They spill their stories before the solid ground can make them fast. They tell of days when the sun never sets or never rises, birds that swim but cannot fly, great fish that sing, of smoking mountains, shrieking ice, forests where men become trees, one-footed men, dog-headed men, waves as high as cathedral bells, seas as still as death. They have sailed so far they have gazed at unfamiliar stars and wondered how they are to find their way back.

She replenishes the wine, sharpens quills. Their salty eyes, narrowed as horizons, navigate the billows of her dress, each swell and dip, seeking always somewhere to make landfall, claim dominion.

They go, at last, to wives or mistresses. She puts the shutters up and bars the door. Her father rubs his milky eyes, pushes away the notes he can no longer read, unrolls the vellum. The grid is ready; the compass rose points north.

She takes the quill. Her father puts his hand over hers. Together, they fix the stories they have heard. The feather swoops, charts the safe harbour, skirts the reef. This is where she will paint the puffing winds, here devouring monsters, there pattern those strange constellations. Beyond this line, nothing; the map waits.

The mapmakers work late in the closed room, conjuring from ink and skin new worlds neither will ever see.

Undelivered

They call us for breakfast in the half-light. Four more empty chairs today, Ma.

We scramble first around seven, back, refuel, rearm. They bring us sandwiches. We scramble again, then a third. At dusk, those of us who are left stay on readiness. They want us to fly at night now we are so few. Porter nodded off in his cockpit. When I do sleep, my mind still flies.

Peter presses his wedding ring into my hand. 'Send her this,' he says. 'I know I won't be coming back.'

I visit Johnny. His feet are burnt, and his hands are burnt. His nose, eyes, lips.

I watch Burrell nosedive into the waves.

We say we're not scared, but who in England ever prayed for bad weather? We pray very hard. The sky stays blue as eternity.

I will never send you this, Ma.

Glorious weather. That's all I can say.

Hide

Nothing stirs.

He dresses in the bathroom without turning on the light or stopping to wash the sweat from his skin. His wife, used to him slipping away, folds toward the hollow on his side of the bed but doesn't wake.

He pauses for a second outside his daughter's room. All he can see in the glow of the nightlight is a tumble of fake fur on the bed. But he can hear her soft snuffle rise and fall. At this hour, it is the loudest sound in the house, muffling the hum of the fridge. It doesn't silence the incessant hissing in his ears.

His bag is packed, ready, by the door. He eases the key, steps from warm to cold.

It is still some time until dawn.

He picks his way up the path to the wicket gate. The light is beginning to line the horizon as he walks into the wood.

They chose this house because of the forest. It was spring when they came to view, the trees a spellbinding ring of green leaves, birdsong and the scent of bluebells. Like Sleeping Beauty's castle, he told his daughter. He knows this only because his wife and daughter repeat it, a favourite story. It's not the sort of thing he remembers, these days. He pictures the ancient woodland wrapping around his girl until someone proves brave enough and strong enough to protect her. He no longer believes he is that man, nor perhaps that any such man exists.

He never sleeps soundly here. His memory crashes in like the bad fairy at Beauty's christening, uninvited but impossible to turn away.

It stalks him now down to the hide, flashing its slideshow across the screen of trees in starbursts of white, black and red. His tinnitus revs up to screaming pitch, like jets or shells, like terrified children.

Crouched in the hide, he waits for the damp and the green to do their work. As dark melts to light, the images flicker away, the noise fades to its relentless but familiar whistle. He breathes in. It is the smell he loves most, a slow, ripe decay, time taking the time it should.

They emerge as if developing from the mist. The hinds first, then the stag, antlers pricking through the branches. They turn towards him.

It is the shot of a lifetime. He prepares, focuses, then lowers his camera. A shutter-click and they will be gone. This one he will cache in his mind's eye, the gift the good fairy gave to lighten the curse.

He will return to the desert soon. Last night, his wife asked why he always takes such risks, why face such horror again. Someone must bear witness, he said. But he's not sure that's the reason. The thorns stick too deep in his skin now; he is too tangled to go forward or back.

The deer dissolve from the glade.

Time lapses.

Nothing stirs.

By Ear

Anything you could sing, Harry could play. Every knees-up, there he'd be, glass after glass rattling on top of the old joanna, us lining them up too fast for him to drink, all roaring along, sobbing into our beer at the sad ones.

First to go, Harry was, down the street, flags out, band playing, strict march. They all went eventually. Some came back. Harry last of all.

He'll nurse that pint all night, head shaking like some great bee's buzzing round.

What Harry hears now, I can't tell. I hauled the piano into the yard, let the boys smash it up.

Resistance

All summer, he has kept the blades sharp, the leather supple, rubbing in wax until his own skin starts to split. Harder to keep himself in shape. The untrained muscles in his calves are softening, that crouching balance slowly tipping askew without the resistance of the ice.

When Anna tells him of the latest proclamation, he doesn't comprehend at first, distracted by a distant sound like glass splintering.

'We must get rid of them, sweetheart.' She squats by his chair, makes him look at her. 'Hide them, at least.'

After they take the children to school, they lever up the floorboards in the hall cupboard. He lays his skates down among the dry dust and cobwebs.

'These too.' Anna holds out his medals, still in their frame from the sideboard. 'If they come, they'll only take them. Besides. Who knows?' She hesitates. 'We might need them. For barter.'

He wraps them in a worn tablecloth Anna hands him. Their heft takes him back, the unexpected weight of solid gold. He is on the podium once again, the flag rising, band playing, all eyes on him and his golden victories. He replaces the boards as if sealing some ancient chieftain's tomb.

~

The occupiers had come in the spring; overnight, like an unseasonal blizzard that leaves the dawn indistinct and unfamiliar. As the summer light lengthens, the town is closed down. Businesses are seized, travel restricted. The shops are emptied, the parks turned over to vegetable beds. Papers must be shown; a curfew is set. Shots are heard in suburban streets. Doors slam at night, and in the morning, people are gone. When the days darken, when the lake freezes, skating is forbidden.

He must teach other sports now. Gymnastics, wrestling: games of curves and claustrophobic warmth. He trains his players to twist and clutch. He feels their breath hot on his cheek, the damp closeness of their bodies. He yearns for the cold solidity of the ice, the solitary freedom found in speed of his own making.

~

'I saw Erik today.'

Anna spoons out four careful portions of stew. He sees how little she has served herself, forks one of his potatoes towards her plate, but she shakes her head.

'He asked after you. Said it would be good to catch up.' She meets his eyes for a second as she lifts the empty casserole from the table.

'Erik?' he says. 'Yes. It's been a while.'

Secrets flicker across the town like the northern lights. Secrets about men like Erik. Some have already gone into the mountains. Boys he was at school with, friends whose deep voices he used to hear in church. They move on the enemy through the endless winter dark, shrouded like ghosts and bearing the white touch of death.

He has been sounded out before: careful conversations started after Sunday service or in the changing room. He has pretended not to understand. His life is not his to risk, he reasons. He is a husband, a father; he has responsibilities.

'Finding the time,' he says. 'My teaching. And the curfew, of course.'

Anna tells the children to eat up while it's hot.

It is a shock to him, his cowardice. He has been a hero in this town. He has hurtled down hardened rivers, his life suspended on a silver sliver of speed, ice spitting in his face, the deadly cold fragile inches away. But it has smothered him, this grey-uniformed avalanche of terror. When he passes the soldiers in the street, he looks away. Erik, he imagines, only holds his head higher.

While Anna takes the children to her mother's, he raises the boards. He lifts out his skates, removes the guard, runs his thumb along the edge. He pulls up the tongue, laces each boot tight enough to hold him straight. His steps ring hollow on the thick pine as he stalks the floor. He totters, flops back heavy in his chair before he spoils the naked blades against the wood.

~

The winter thickens. Now people talk to him mostly of the weather and the scarcity of fish. He no longer knows how Anna spends her days. Coming home early one afternoon, he spots her, turning a corner, in earnest conversation with a man who looks like Erik. In the evenings, she takes her knitting upstairs to sit with the Larsens once the children are asleep.

He hears the riddle of the Larsens' fire overhead, pictures the three of them, hands out to the warmth. He wants to put his ear to his own stove, thinks he catches his wife's voice down the scalding pipe.

'Not the man I married...'

The room feels unbearably hot.

~

The blackout blankets the town. Still, the snowlight forces him into the shadows; they used to call this a hunter's moon, now it is named for bombers.

When he reaches the lake, the wind is rising. The sound of snow slipping from branches ripples like faraway applause. Before him, the ice inks blue-black. For the first time in his life, he wonders whether it will bear him.

He needs ice the thickness of his hand. But this might be frazil, freezing too fast and easy to fracture. In normal times, he would know. He has not been paying enough attention.

He steps out. The shrapnel air cuts his cheeks. He flexes his knees, bends deeper into the unaccustomed ache. *Dip, slide.* Cold captures his lungs. *Dip, glide.* Memory tremors through his legs. *Dip, slide, dip, glide...*

And he is away, leaving the friction of his fear on the shore, the swoop and sway of his body looping round and round the lake, his ears humming wild with the race of his own blood. Across the glassy stillness, he etches rings of rediscovered triumph.

When that first crack booms, he never knows whether it is a gunshot or the ice breaking under him that brings him crashing down.

Gelsenkirchen: 10/10ths Cloud, Thirty Aircraft Lost

In memoriam Doug Telfer, died 26 June 1943, aged 19 years

Zum-zum! The air shatters to shrapnel, white-hot, the compass spirals, the charts flake, and he is thrown from unrelenting close-cabined judder and thrum into the gape of night.

In that second's freefall, above the wounded city, he can navigate no further forward, find no path across imagined blueprints of unbuilt bridges, beside his sweetheart and their never-born children.

Instead, he reaches back, mapping through melting muscle, bone, feeling for warm eggs under backyard chickens, the Airedale's downy muzzle, his baby brother's cherub curls, reaches for the cool consoling fingers of his mother.

Mother.

Mum.

Black Market

'What'll it be? Petrol, pills, ID?'

He was sitting in the darkest, smokiest corner, this friend of a friend of Freddy's who could get you anything.

Under my arm, Mitzi's little heart was beating fast.

'A soul,' I whispered. 'I need a new soul.'

The tip of his cigarette glowed red.

'Takes longer.' He exhaled. 'And it'll cost.'

I slid the envelope across. He pulled it to him.

'Something more than that,' he said.

Mitzi licked my ear, whimpered.

Today I skip through the blackout and the blitzed streets, whistling childhood songs I thought I'd forgotten.

I walk alone. I had to get rid of Mitzi. Everything's better now, apart from this sudden, inexplicable terror of dogs.

How I Became a Star

They will say it was the sway of my hip, my hair's lustre, that gleam of sweat beading my spine. Or they will call me, only, beautiful. What more could you need to know of me, after all? In truth, I was a girl like any other, dipping my pitcher in the dappled river, dreaming those dawn-rubied droplets jewels, a burbling fool, babbling as the birds themselves fell silent, as even the water's dimpled flow slowing, slowing... stopped.

Look! Look up! On the far bank – there – steam-snort of breath, the flehmen curl, branches that twist, then step from the tree. My heart beats once: fabulous beast! Twice, and I know the truth of him by the infinity in his black eye.

And crashes, shatters my pitcher as scrumble, stumble, I scramble – and the drenching wave of his plunge – and my toes sliding, mud sucks, slipping slime – he has come before – yessss, up, hah, running – come for my sisters, in his shifting shapes – oh my treacherous skirts snaring – and the thrud of hooves quakes the air – nothing, nothing to – 'Mother...!' – hold, throw, stab – 'Help me, Mother!' – she snatched, I saw, seized their sweet selves from him, recast... iris swallow laurel... see... See...! she greens my fingers opening tips bud but too, now? no, too late, no, too his hot musk blasts my scalp tines tear my skin and I am down and the agony of his power roots me and I am splintered.

My tardy goddess gathers what is left and hangs me blazing in the cold sky. She means it as a kindness in her way, but now their ceaseless observation will not let me be. They tell my story, pin me to their maps, probe my glare with their bleak gaze as I circle through the mute, eternal dark.

It is not my fault I caught the eye of a god.

Nomad

Home is always someone else's.

Someone else's sofa, spare room if he's lucky, someone else's floor more than once. Someone else's sheets, the sickly scent of someone else's washing powder. Someone else's post-code, tube stop, corner shop. Someone else's neighbour's cat. Someone else's front path, front door, someone else's spare key.

Someone else's cereal bowl, someone else's fucking Man U mug. Someone else's wedding on the wall, someone else's daughter's drawings stuck to someone else's fridge. Someone else's choice of box set. Someone else's time for bed.

Someone else's clock ticking through the still small hours, someone else's radiator clanking into life. Someone else's window overlooking someone else's street.

Someone else's whispers in the next room, walking into someone else's silence. Someone else's invite down someone else's local, someone else's 'I'll get these, mate', someone else's quiet word, someone else's need for space – 'you know, if it was up to me, mate, but the wife...'

Someone else's name crossed off, someone else's phone number, someone else's favour called in, someone else's goodwill.

Only the bag and the pain are his.

Birdman

He hunches over the blank paper, conscious of their sharp eyes on him through the grille.

He examines his hands. Time has barked and gnarled them like birds' feet.

They have become his grandfather's hands.

The grille flicks shut.

His fingers peck at the top sheet, lift and turn it under the harsh light of the bare bulb. He folds. This way, that. He cocks his head, pressing down creases, sharpening angles the way his grandfather taught him. He nips a last point.

It perches on the table, a crisp, white bird.

He takes a second sheet, makes another, then another, until lights out when darkness falls like a thick, black cloth.

Months go by. When his pad runs out, he takes whatever comes to hand. Yellowing headlines screech into herring gulls. Tattered pin-ups plump their partridge breasts. Round the walls creep tiny wrens, cigarette-paper thin. Gossiping sparrows bustle from the library's dog-eared *Oliver Twist*. His lawyer's letters swivel frowning heads, a parliament of owls around the lavatory bowl. From a shining chocolate wrapper – precious, rare – struts a peacock.

The roosts around the cell fill up.

The day his appeal comes through, the door clangs open.

Out fly the birds, clamouring in murmurations, their wings beating like flags, lining the handrails, preening, whistling, massing on the safety nets, calling like swifts gathering to migrate.

Them Flowers in the Dark

Dear Mrs Speirs

I wanted to write you before but had no paper. I think about you a lot. I think about the summer all them flowers with long names. You said what they were. I forget the names but they were dead pretty blue & red & yellow all mixed up like but dead clever so it looked right. I think about them then when its dark the flowers.

Sorry if this is wrong. I dont know when I wrote a letter last it were at school most like. I get lessons about writing here. I work hard. I want to do better.

I hope Sammy is OK & plays with that ball I got him. I nicked it from that other place me & Dobbo were working. I didnt buy it I feel bad about that. You all thinking I got it special.

I think of Emmy with that ball Sammy barking like a right loon the sun behind her like she were a leaf – all light like. When its dark I see her like shes right there by the door. In that dress the yellow one like her hair. Its gone lights out may be but I see her plain as day right there.

I have to say where she is. They go on & on it does my head in. Why wont I tell them where she is. It ud help me. It ud help you. I cant tell no one. You know I cant but that doctor dont shut up posh bitch. You know we have to keep her safe you know shes safe now. Theres no one like her all soft & the world so hard but shes safe now. Thats what I wanted to say really. That & the flowers.

Yours truly

Darren

Mr Punch in Love

You slip a hand into her warm, dark inside. Her head nods heavy under your fingertips. You twist her to you. She bows to your touch. Her body folds soft around your arm. Her painted eyes hold yours, but she stays silent.

'That's the way to do it,' you whisper.

Down the Rabbit Hole

Mr Rabbit was bored.

'How long must we sit here?' he grumbled.

Alice tugged at her sister's sleeve. Donna unhooked an ear-bud.

'Can we go?'

'Soon, hun,' said Donna. 'Just waiting for someone.' She checked her phone. 'They're late.'

Mr Rabbit gave Alice one of his looks. Donna was always waiting for someone.

Alice and Mr Rabbit sat and stared at the river. It was thick and brown. 'Like poo!' shouted Mr Rabbit. 'Ssshh!' giggled Alice

'Let's explore,' said Mr Rabbit. He hated sitting still, even for five minutes.

Alice and Mr Rabbit hopped alongside the wall. She thought it was beautiful, painted all over with bright colours and swirling shapes.

Where the wall ended, a hedge grew. Someone, or something, had made a tunnel through it.

'Let's go in!' cried Mr Rabbit.

Curious, Alice took one step into the hole.

'Further, further,' cried Mr Rabbit. 'It's an adventure!'

Green closed about them. As they tiptoed to where the tunnel curved out of sight, she had the strangest feeling that she was getting smaller. The tunnel rustled and whispered and creaked. A prickle ran up her back. Like someone's watching, she thought and spun round. Nothing. But now she was racing back, out into the light.

'God, Alice Don't disappear like that,' said Donna. 'Look, here's Ryan. He's got you some chocolate.'

'Cowardy custard!' yelled a furious Mr Rabbit, dangling ears down from Alice hand. 'Cowardy, cowardy custard!' But Alice was eating her chocolate and, just for now, no one was listening.

If We Could Knock Through

The floor in the back bedroom was scattered with stones and glass.

'Kids,' said Sophie, stepping round the pieces to the window. 'To be expected, I suppose, it's been empty so long. We'll have to get this boarded up.'

The room was barely furnished, just a single bed, tightly made up with blankets, and a large, old-fashioned wardrobe in dark wood. A damp smell of rotting leaves seeped in through the broken panes.

'Beautiful view of the garden,' said Sophie. 'The boys would just love a swing like that. That one's lethal, though. Look how frayed that rope is.'

Mark came up beside her, rubbing hard at the white scar on his right palm.

'Careful, darling. Watch where you're putting your feet with that glass.' Sophie ran a fingernail along the frame. 'These windows will need replacing anyway.' She turned her attention back inside. 'It's a good size. Whose room was this?'

'My brother's,' said Mark. Under the old oak, the swing swayed slightly, back and forth, as if someone had just this moment jumped away.

'Oh, Jamie's.'

'No.'

'There's that box room next door. I wonder if we could knock through.' Sophie's voice faded as she walked back onto the landing. 'Make a lovely big room, then, perhaps an en suite.'

The heavy curtains didn't stir, but through the broken window, a cold breeze touched Mark's cheek. He started at the sharp rap of knuckles: Sophie tapping hard against the thin partition. Jagged rips in the wallpaper fluttered, where posters had been torn down. The wind was getting up, flattening the treetops to white, agitating the swing. He felt his brother's hands hard on his back, pushing him higher and higher until he begged to be let off; the same hands forcing him down on his face.

'You know, there's a lot we could do with this place. Heaps of potential.' Sophie came back in, flopping onto the bed with a bounce. 'Can't think why you've never mentioned it.' Mark winced at the high-pitched squeaking of the springs. His palm stung. He had rubbed the weal red.

'Hang on.' Sophie leaned up on one elbow. 'What do you mean, not Jamie's? You've only got one brother.'

Mark bent, picked up a piece of broken brick. Fragments of glass dotted his hand with blood, but he didn't feel the spike. Nor did he pay any attention to Sophie's cry as he twisted towards the window and hurled chunk after chunk through each remaining pane, the shards flying out into the garden like a flock of birds beaten up for the guns.

There Was No Possibility of Taking a Walk That Day

The sirens had blared at 5 a.m. She was up with the baby anyway, so she'd gone round closing each vent. Ken slept right through, as he always did. She couldn't think when she had last slept so deeply.

At 7:30, Ken kissed her goodbye, and she took the baby into the bathroom, flicking on the purifier. She heard Ken zip up his vent suit and slip out the front door. She set her phone for the regulatory ten minutes. She watched each second count down.

By lunchtime, the monitor displayed levels safe enough to wind up the shutters. They were lucky to have such an elevated apartment, thanks to Ken's family. She would have gone onto the balcony, but the levels were still too high for the baby. And besides, the baby wanted feeding, again.

She looked down at the yellow smog line. Beneath it, people were going about their business, strapped in their vent suits, moving through the airlocks into air-controlled offices and shops. She had been part of that world once, she thought, but she wasn't sure.

Still the baby in her arms wouldn't settle. In and out of each room she paced, first this way, then that. Finally, she put the baby down and stood by the balcony door, staring at the skyline.

By 4 p.m., it was dark.

When the all-clear sounded an hour later, for a few moments it drowned out the sound of the baby crying.

The Firestarters

Soon we all knew about it, what had happened in the valleys beyond the next valley to ours.

It was the pedlar who told us, of course. As always, we heard him coming long before we saw him, the clatter of pots and pans ringing high off the sharp-faced crags. The children bounded to him, like kids round a nanny goat.

He stopped by the market cross, took the beer Jenell had ready for him. Then he began unwrapping his bundles, seeming as surprised as we were at what he revealed. He fluttered ribbons at the young women; the children pestered for sweetmeats, toys. All of us had things we needed, salt, needles, thread, blades. But most of all we hungered for news.

He told us the usual stories, where the sickness had been, which lords had died, which ladies married, an unexpected harvest of apricots or haul of fish, juicy riches we could only taste in dreams. We shook our heads at the things the townsfolk did. We waited. He always saved the best for last.

The children skipped away with their shiny tops and poppets. He dropped his voice, so we must close in to hear.

It had started with one or two, he said, fearsome to look at. Skin like polished coal – and the size of them! All males, they had come, rumour had it, in search of mates. Shudders from some of the women, frowns from more of the men. The pedlar leant back. Still, those first ones had seemed harmless enough. But more had come. And more. And then the fires had started. Roofs set ablaze, houses gone, whole streets in some villages, that's what they said. And worst of all, he had heard this on the road, in one place, a winter's worth of grain. He had feared for his wares, sought caves to sleep in. A man needed to know his trade was safe. No, he hadn't seen them himself. He had been glad to keep moving, to keep ahead of them.

Emmett said, yes, he remembered now seeing smoke from out that way not so long ago when he'd been up cutting the first hay.

There had been a dark cloud, said Ancel, high in the sky. He had thought it birds migrating early.

Her grandfather had spoken of seeing such things when he was a boy, said Jenell.

The next day the pedlar left, the sound of his going the last of him to leave. We gathered again round the cross. We had not slept, most of us, gazing up at our rafters, the familiar smell from our own careful, damped-down fires suddenly strong in our nostrils.

Thanks be, we gave our house of worship a wooden roof, said Aldous.

We should not panic, said Fabian. You know what tales pedlars tell. They sugar their goods with stories to sweeten us to buy.

Your house, too, Fabian, has wooden tiles, said Emmett. You have less to fear than most of us. Some raised eyebrows at such disrespect. Others muttered agreement.

Viveka said we should ask Kai. He could see further, up on the high slopes with the goats, reach his long looping call to the goatherds in the other valleys, ask what they knew.

We could send a boy up to him, said Jenell.

But that would be too late, said Emmett. They might come at any time. They were already on their way. We must be prepared.

We should have water ready, said Ancel. And rakes to pull down burning straw.

Have we so much water we can spare buckets to sit in the sun? Emmett said.

Tell us your plan then, Emmett, said Fabian, folding his arms.

We must stop the fires from starting, Emmett said. So we must stop the fire-starters.

Now, in the hottest days of summer, we feel the thunder gather and press. By day, we watch the skies. At night, our bodies ache from harvest, but we cannot sleep. Under our sloping thatch, we lie, eyes wide in the relentless summer light. We do not dream; instead, we hear the old stories whispered long ago by the winter hearth. How, at Thor's command, they will open their cruel jaws, take up hot embers, spread those coal-black wings and fly. How they will let the fire fall down on those who have offended him.

We are God-fearing people; we put our trust in the Lord. We thought we had left such tales behind. But these are creatures of the savage gods. They do not live by mercy and pity as we do. We must protect ourselves. This is the last valley; there is nowhere else for us to go. When they come, we will be ready. We will be waiting with our nets and our stones and our hammers.

The Sweetest Poison Kills You Slowest

All London adores Eliza's parrot, save Mary Durdy who cannot abide a caged bird. Eliza slips it nips of sugar, commanding it to talk. It whistles at her like a furious kettle.

Eliza locks the tea caddy and sits, straight-backed in her stiff brocade. Her parlour glows in the spitting light of its well-fed fire. It is a haven. Everyone says so. When Mary Durdy comes, in her grey gown, it feels as though a cloud has stolen in from the street.

Eliza pours. Samuel steps forward, passes the cup to where Mary Durdy perches, drizzling her persistent sermons.

'Will you take a little sugar, Mary,' Eliza asks, 'against the bitterness?'

Samuel offers the bowl as if it were a scoop of diamonds. He is a magnificent creature, Eliza thinks. His red coat blazes, bright as the bird. She has powdered his hair with white, swaddled his legs in silk. His life is sweeter here, surely, whatever Mary Durdy says, than in the salt sweat of Papa's plantation.

Mary Durdy declines, drones something Eliza does not care to catch about decay and rot. The parrot sidles up the bars of its cage. Samuel retreats to the wall.

Soon Eliza will be Lady Poole. Time, then, to leave behind the tedious duties of childhood. Such as entertaining Mary

Durdy. Eliza dips her spoon into the bowl, glimpses in its sparkle the jewels she has been promised.

'Sugar!'

Mary Durdy starts, slops tea into her saucer. 'Sugar! Sugar!' shrills the bobbing parrot. Eliza claps in triumph, rewards it with another sliver, sucks it a kiss from her pursed lips.

Mary Durdy, after merely the briefest pause, recommences. Eliza sighs and stirs her tea to glittering sweetness. She smoothes her India cashmere, admires the way the firelight plays across its rich gold threads. It shows their colour off just so.

Samuel, as a good footman should, says nothing, eyes fixed ahead. As evening falls, he watches his face emerge, reflected on the window like an unforgiving ghost glaring in through the pane.

Eating the Zoo

The city gates were barred, the railways blockaded, the last telegraph line cut. But if we could no longer feed the animals, Jean-Jacques said, the animals could at least still feed us.

At first we feasted. We could afford to be generous too, doling out camel *carbonade* to the crowd. In the crush, bowlfuls were knocked to the ground, steaming and wasted. Jean-Jacques ordered the turnstiles chained after that. There is no trusting a mob, he said, turning away from the gates. The urchins stared in at us, their sallow cheeks pressed to the railings. Their fingers curled around the bars put me in mind of lemurs.

We worked our way steadily through the ungulates. Deer, yak, zebra gave me few qualms. I had to force down the giraffe, however; the memory of those soft lips and liquid eyes spoiled its savour. Our pens and cages began to empty. Snake, I discovered after my initial reluctance, does indeed taste agreeably of chicken.

Chef Choron came calling at our side door. His customers expected meat and had good money to pay for it. Through the window of Jean-Jacques' office, I watched them shake hands. On the ninety-ninth day of the siege, Chef served the *beau monde* royally at his Rue St-Honoré restaurant. *Le civet de kangourou* and bear chops in pepper sauce, washed down with an excellent Mouton Rothschild 1846, Jean-Jacques reported, the smell of cigar smoke hanging on him after his dinner. He found me alone in the echoing bear pit. *Ursidae* have always been my particular study.

The city fell silent. No hooves clattered, no birds sang. At night, our hungry wolves still howled, but no town dogs swelled their mournful chorus, dog being, it seems, a fair substitute for mutton. We would slaughter the wolves when they were weaker, Jean-Jacques said, eyeing their yellow teeth and counting the remaining ammunition.

Our famous elephant shrank in its skin. Forward it shuffled, expecting currant buns and a scratch behind the ears with the stick we held. I looked away. Jean-Jacques raised the gun and toppled it with a single shot. The earth shook when it fell. Elephant is coarse and oily. I cannot recommend it.

The enemy was growing impatient. Shells blasted our walls without cease. All night, I blocked my ears to the screaming from the streets outside and from within. Next morning, the wolves were gone. Beside their gaping enclosure lay what was left of Jean-Jacques, jagged and tooth-scarred, his black coat ripped, his heart torn away.

I can do nothing now but await the end. I sit in the monkey house. They huddle together, regard me with their starving ancient eyes. I hum with emptiness. Monsieur Darwin tells us these are our cousins. We share our churning hunger. I feel they understand me. What monster is it eats its own kin?

Picnic at the End of the World

When the sirens blare, we pedal hard up the hill. We've been paying attention. We chose this spot thirteen weeks ago. In the valley, the roads out of town clog like arteries.

I shake out my mother's snowy damask. You slice the thickening air with your great-aunt's mismatched silver. We lay out the crockery dug from the back of the cupboard, that pattern we loved so much when we put it on the wedding list but now can't remember why.

We unpack the hamper and begin to eat...

...sourdough kick-started with a culture that bubbled westwards across Europe one step ahead of advancing armies, your Grandma's pastry which we never tasted but everyone said was the best ever, crumpled bags of caramels my mother craved while she was carrying me, hedgehog cake with almond prickles and five candles, the biggest juiciest bramble you thought you couldn't reach but which was worth every scratchy snag, that chocolate Easter bunny too beautiful to bite without weeping, sherbet dib dabs and white mice and flying saucers, tiny bottles of summer-curdled-winter-slushed milk, rice pudding with skin on for the last day of term, fluffy mints from Grandad's pocket, leftover Yorkshires gilded with syrup, a licked-out cake bowl, Mum's treacle pudding erupting like a suet Vesuvius, lip-smarting crisps and warm lemonade in the back of the Cortina waiting for the grown-ups outside the pub, mouth-sealing bonfire toffee, bangers on the barbecue half-charred half-pink like sunburnt noses, first kisses cherried with cola, the sudden obvious point of olives and anchovies, the devilish whiff of kidneys, the sour-shock pickle of someone else's body, silky tongues of smoked salmon on Christmas morning, nostrils popping with champagne, Marmite, sleepy-eyed moussaka with chips our first morning barely awake but ravenous at that old-school Greek place that's a sushi bar now, bitter aniseed that kept us dancing well past dawn, salt-rimed-lime margaritas under a stardust California sky, gelato masking the June sewer stink of honeymoon Venice, the wake-up chilli spike of breakfast in Kerala, the peace of tofu in your vegan phase, falling for the irresistible temptation of bacon sandwiches after an all-nighter, peat-smoke whisky burning away the heartbreak of the child who came too soon, amazing tea and buttered toast after the child who arrived right on time, cook's-perk crackling chicken skin stripped from the carcass by the kitchen sink, wasabi's eye-opening sting, the never-to-be-repeated-twelve-course-tasting-menu-treat from your father before you stopped talking to each other altogether, those oh-so-expensive Valentine truffles that tasted almost better than sex, HobNobs in bed to the Sunday clatter of rain and bells, three strawberries of perfect ripeness picked with my father in the care home garden, Mars Bars on the moors still a sodden drenching hour's hike from the bloody car, cold beer, takeaways family-style with friends, warm beer, pastries dunked in gossipy lattes, soldiers dripping thick with yolk, a long glass of cool clear water downed in one...

We raise our toast in our one surviving crystal glass. It glints like ice against the dropping sun. As the earth cracks and the sea rises and the sky falls, nothing has ever tasted so sweet.

Even to the Edge of Doom

Strangers come two days before market with ladders and faces sharp as axes. One bids my Margaret cover her golden hair for shame. But his eyes slide over her like fat on a skillet, and my belly clenches.

That night, Robin creaks from our bed. When he slips back, his beard specked with dew and his feet nursing my calf for warmth, I do not ask where he has been.

They leave the church door wide while they go about their work. They rejoice in what they do. The town square rings to the sound of their breaking in mocking echo of the Christmas bells that herald our salvation.

Margaret and I carry our heavy baskets home through the churchyard. It is midsummer, but the ground cracks under our feet. Frosted with heaven overnight, the way glisters red and yellow and richest blue. They have swept away the greatest pieces, but Margaret plucks a shard the breadth of my palm from the grass. I hide it in my kerchief. The church windows gape over us, broken-mouthed. The imps grin from the gutters.

By Sunday, they are done. Swifter by far to pull down than to build.

To step into our church was to step into Noah's rainbow. Now it sits white as bone.

The lime is not yet dry. Our familiar angels – O, the fire of their flaming wings! – fade through the thickening mist of the wash. The saints watch, eyeless, faces blasted as though all the winds of time had blown at once. Thomas, James, Catherine, Margaret, Anne, for whom we named our babes, those that grew and those we buried. Peter Glazier will come and set new windows of clear glass, they say. Until then, sparrows clatter and gossip in the high beams.

The priest waits, not beside the stone altar but behind a wooden table. He has the look of a goodwife, in his plain surplice, aproned and ready to spoon out broth. The great silver cross and candlesticks that were our pride are missing.

My elder daughter's husband rises in his black coat. Since he turned to the new religion, all joy is gone from my Catherine's face as if he had taken a hammer to the pane of her and struck it through. The priest steps to one side. It is my son-in-law who speaks. Those who know where the silver has been taken, it is their duty before the king, before the Lord, to declare it. The priest stares over our heads to the west door, to where our Doom was painted. Last Sunday, the crowd of the blessed climbed up to heaven and the wicked tumbled down to hell. This Sunday, the wall is blank.

No voice answers but the sparrows. I do not look at my husband. We fold our hands and lower our eyes. More than saints may lose their heads.

Monday noon, I take cheese and apples and go to my husband where he cuts saplings. I have not done so since the children were small.

The light dapples green and gold. The coppice rushes soft with full leaves and the wings of birds. In the deep hush of the wood, Robin unwraps the treasure so we may see the shine of it one last time. I have not held it before. The silver weighs heavier than I had thought. I touch my lips to the cross, feel the precious metal warm beneath them, then swaddle it well in the oiled cloths and lay it in the chest. Robin nails down the lid.

We dig the pit together. We have chosen a fine old tree to mark the place. We know it by the names we carved when we were courting. It is heavy labour. Afterwards, we unlace and dry the sweat from our skin in the sweet air. The trees arch over us when we kneel. The taste of each other's flesh is salt like good bread. I count the years of us together in the rings of our bodies, the lines around his eyes where he has smiled, the white webs that spider my belly. Afterwards, we whisper that the young king is not strong. We will wait. We will stand fast and grow steady, as the wood has stood.

I walk home with my husband's kisses fresh upon me. My son-in-law struts by my door in his crow's coat, and I bend my head, in the proper manner.

Margaret has washed the glass she saved and placed it on the kitchen sill. The eye of the angel winks in the catching sun.

Caramel Baby

She keeps a quarter of Mary-Jane caramels deep in her handbag, like hidden jewels sewn into a hem. On the bus home, she twists one open, the waxy paper silken in her fingers. It is as sticky as the August heat. The creamy scent makes her mouth water.

She's eating too many, she thinks. Getting fat. Reaches for just one more.

~

Their anniversary falls as the clocks go back and the days darken. A neighbour offers to babysit, a rare treat. They dress up for that new Italian place on the high street. Spaghetti squirms and wriggles from their forks. They giggle like teenagers, the years softening in the Chianti-bottle candlelight. They try not to think of the movement of ships, two empires staring each other down like tomcats on a fence, the world holding its breath. She chooses caramelised oranges from the dessert trolley, closes her eyes as the glistening sugar melts on her tongue, its spun gold as insubstantial as a fairy's wish.

Four days later, the crisis is over. She lets out her waistband, breathes more easily, makes an appointment with the doctor.

On Bonfire Night, she hands out apples, round as her swelling belly and enamelled with brittle sweetness. The burst of rockets sets the unplanned, unexpected baby kicking. The guy is burning to his ragged bones. Despite the fire's blaze, her scorching cheeks, she shivers. How close her children came to this.

~

December is smothered by fog. She steams the kitchen in clouds of hefty tenderness in reply – stew and dumplings, steak and kidney, treacle pudding. The largest portion for her husband, the children next, the last for herself and the tadpole baby. The bubbling syrup scalds her lips like a volcanic kiss.

Snow falls on Boxing Day. It will be three months before they see green again. Their breath glazes the bedspread with ice. She scratches baby names on the frost inside the window. It is the coldest winter for a generation. She dresses the children by the gas fire in the lounge, rubbing love into their arms and legs then swaddling them tight with layers of wool. The icicles hanging from the school roof are as long as her five-year-old.

She flicks on Housewives' Choice and rests her swollen ankles, bracing herself for home-time pick-up, the chill trudge there and back again. She works her way through a bag of Keiller's butterscotch, absent-mindedly concertinas each glossy discarded wrapper into a fan. Matt Munro sings 'When Love Comes Along', his voice like honey.

~

The snow goes suddenly at the end of March, like an exorcised ghost. The children hunt eggs in the back garden. She spits on her hanky, wipes away chocolate beards. The golden snouts of late daffodils snuffle out. Something is stirring.

The baby arrives with no fuss, five days after Easter. The midwife lifts it from her like pulling toffee. She kisses the top of its buttery head. It tastes as sweet as hope.

Renovation

'Sorry, hard hats on, please.'

Their entrance had disturbed the air. Dust motes spiralled, a double helix in the shafts of sun.

'It's actually much more structurally sound than it looks. But got to keep the Health and Safety chaps happy...'

She had expected damp and mustiness. Instead, warmth swaddled her. She thought she could smell baking bread.

'...once one of the most important houses in town... Oh, you've seen the Pevsner entry? That fireplace, of course. Marvellous.'

The leaded lights scattered the floor with diamonds. At the edge of her eye, she saw something flicker, but when she turned her head, it had gone.

'Yes, we understand the council will be very sympathetic. All sorts of grants available...'

At each tread, the wood gave a little, then rocked gently back. Nothing in the house was still.

'Do mind the stairs. The floors have all been treated, but it's still very uneven!'

There were wings around her head, a beating of wings up into the sun. She felt as light as air.

'The pigeons have made themselves at home, I'm afraid. Soon sorted, though, once the roof's done...'

A down feather settled at her feet. Deep inside, she sensed something shift.

'I say, steady there... All right? As I said, the floors... All part of the charm...'

She would take the test when they got home, but already she knew. Time opened up before her.

Health and Pleasure, Glorious Sea!

When had she last been truly naked? She could not remember. Miss Miller blushed even to think the word. In the nursery, she thought. Below her, the waves hushed and sifted.

It seemed an impossibility, to be standing here, her white body facing her black dress in the half-light. The wooden walls creaked like stays. Without her scaffold of bodice, petticoat, corset, she feared she would collapse. So many days of packing-cases and hessian had left her powdered with dust like a moth's wing. Her modest trunks and bandboxes despatched to her new home with Aunt Marlowe. The weeks before spent stripping The Cedars, hauling down heavy velvet with Betty and Susan, beating carpets, sorting furniture for sale. Papa, first to be parcelled away in his box of gleaming mahogany, still a presence like cobwebs she could not reach.

She pulled on her costume. Could she step outside in such a manner, her white shins glaring like peeled twigs? But Aunt Marlowe had insisted on it: nothing surpassed sea bathing for the nerves. And all her life, Miss Miller had done as she was told.

The door was so swollen in its frame, she must put her weight to it, tottering as it swung open, one hand up against the brilliant sun.

She descended with care, the ladder trembling at the incessant rub of waves. Sand rasped her ankles, seeped between her sinking toes. She could not stand still. She must choose either to retreat or go into the sea.

The swell rolled up, then away, wrapping close round her calves, thighs, waist, and then retreating, tugging the heavy cotton back. She calmed herself, counting, steady, one, two, three, four...

When the breaker smacked her, she went under. The current whipped her like seaweed. Her hands scrabbled without purchase. She could hear nothing, see nothing, say nothing.

When the undertow let her go, she found herself facing the horizon, bathing cap gone, her hair a long, dripping cord. Her ears roared. A new sound spluttered, distant, strange. It came to her that it was laughter, her own.

Now she waded deeper, letting the water take her weight, submerging, emerging, each dip timed with the motion of the waves. Old words washed back to her. *White horses.* Who had taught her that? Nurse? Her mother?

Dressing again was a trial. The cloth caught at her damp flesh, her fingers fumbled pins and ties. She combed her sand-heavy hair as best she could. Her wrinkled hands refused gloves.

Seawater was already frilling her hem white as she stepped back up the beach. Her legs and arms rippled with the memory of the sea. Deep in the folds, tiny grains of sand pricked and polished her skin at each stride. She glowed so, she thought all must see the pink beaming through the mourning black. A soft breeze blew. Moistening her lips with her tongue, she tasted the intense, savoury tang of salt.

Rockpooling

'Look, Daddy, look!'

She strains upwards, on tiptoes, arm, fingers, whole body outstretched, willing him to see.

The black pebble gleams in her starfish hand.

'I found some jet.' She plants it in his palm.

'That's not jet!' Her brother pulls at his sleeve, trying to get a better look. 'It's not, is it, Dad?'

'Well, it does look like jet.' Unlikely, he thinks, and too heavy. 'Let's see what else we can find.'

They lean their long shadows over the pool. He takes his daughter's hand. Her sea-pruned fingers curl round his like suckers. Last summer, he had held onto her brother as tightly. Now the boy crouches at the edge, old enough to balance on his own.

The green weed sways softly. A crab scuttles under the overhang. He names mussels for them. Barnacles. Sea squirts. They giggle at the words. Twice a day, he says, the waves come in and wash the pool clean. No one but them will ever see it just like this again.

He glances up. The tide has turned, sooner than he'd expected.

'I know what we should try to find now.' They look up, their faces like sea anemones, opening for what he will say next. 'Mummy! And what was Mummy going to get?'

'Ice cream!'

The boy is already away. Hoisting his daughter onto his shoulders, he strides after, calling warnings of seaweed and slippery rocks.

The pebble, drying now to grey, lies forgotten, as the tide creeps in behind them.

Sea Change

My heart sank.

I watched it go. It fought hard to keep afloat. I took my boathook, knocked back its jellyfish pulses. I had to make sure. Cracked, it bubbled silver as it dropped, an aspirin fizz then one toxic gulp like mercury breaking from a thermometer. It stopped struggling after that, twisted, turned in the tug of the tide, spiralling slowly down into the deep dark.

I watched until I could see it no more.

My mother warned me. You never know when you might want it back. To shut her up, I marked it by the harbour buoy. I knew I wouldn't need it again. I crossed off years well enough without it, the sea coming in, going out, working, eating, sleeping. Except on stormy nights. The wild clamour of the buoy bell woke me then. I'd hug the pillow over my ears and curse my mother.

But she was right. Of course.

There you were, one day, end of the pier, leaning into the wind like a figurehead. For the first time since I drowned my heart, I licked my roughened, seaside lips and tasted salt.

That night, I rowed out and let down my net. I threw back the crabs and the mackerel, rubbed off the barnacle crust by the light of the moon. My pearlescent heart shone, strange, hard, beautiful.

I bent my back to the oars and headed for land, heart thumping like a fresh-caught fish.

Downhill

There is only one hill in Cambridge. She lived at the top.

Every evening after work, he toiled up Castle Street.

Every morning, he freewheeled down, King of the Mountains.

It was an uphill task, even so.

The October mist rising from the river caught his breath. He arrived on her step scattered with dew diamonds. She drew him into the warmth.

In January, beaten by the Siberian wind, he got off and pushed. Her lips salved his raw face.

By April, he was toning up. 'Shall I ask her...?' he thought, as she brushed pink cherry petals from his hair. '...Soon.'

Come August, he barely broke sweat. If his heart pounded, that was the weight of the tiny box in his pocket.

The studious biochemist who answered the door couldn't say exactly where she'd gone. 'Harvard, maybe? America, for sure.'

He turned around. At the bottom of the hill, tourists clambered from the last punts of the day. He wobbled his way through the crowds, back into the stone heart of the city.

Ancient bells tolled the hour.

Already the first leaves were flushing red.

Walking on Eggshells

It starts here. A hairline crack, a heave, a bursting open. Peeping fanfare and a sudden crown. New life hatching in the palm of your hand. Fragile. Miraculous. Possible. A puff of gold.

Maybe it began before. An upturned basket, smash of yolk across flagstones, a fist. Another door walked into. Practised make-up over a sunset face. A brittle mask hardening.

Perhaps as long ago as this. The shiny ring too tight, the arm too close around your waist, the hissed instruction. *Smile.* That shiver of doubt icing your spine. That starched white eggshell of a dress.

Motel Road Trip Honeymoon Postcards

Room 7 They're woken by an earnest burble, like aliens giggling, a tinny clatter of claws across the roof. Raccoons. Spooned together in the dark, they hold their breath with delight.

Room 3 No shower, the manager sniffs, like it's their fault. What do they care, still high on the rub and stickiness of each other? On the empty beach, a small boy dances barefoot. His father doesn't look up from the business news, leaves his son's shoes behind when they go. When we have children, they vow, we will tell them every day how much we love them.

Room 12b Every nine minutes, on the concrete landing, the ice machine grinds. The season's over; the big dipper chained up. They see no one but feel watched. They have come too far south. He mutes the TV while she sleeps, finds only the weather channel or, weirdly, a single swimmer ploughing relentless ten-yard lengths. He wonders if he's done the right thing.

Room 18 He throws up all night. Oysters. Their first. She frets about hospitals, insurance, the five thousand miles home. Invisible neighbours thud, crash, door-slam for hours. She imagines them doing – what? Dividing booty, dismembering bodies? By morning, he's wrung out, but okay.

Room 9 They choose the room overlooking the forest with its tall trees and actual bears. From the headland, they spot – way out – a grey smudge. A whale! Its slow migration seems like a blessing.

Room 1 They have visited the ghost town, the ancient lake. On the porch, they drink makeshift margaritas under the Milky Way. Stars scatter, thick as spilled salt, the light outfacing the dark. Reality feels a galaxy away. Fourteen years later, during the divorce, this is the night each will remember, never knowing how the constellations of their memories aligned.

Modern Love

She counts his heartbeats, knows each step he takes. Better than yesterday, not as good as last week. His red line tracks the grid, leading her up one street, sharp turn down the avenue, spiking like a market in meltdown.

They make sure to share meals – his eggs over easy, her cheese and pickle sandwich. The brightness of the food startles them, makes each greedy for the other's unfiltered colours.

She is glazing over at a PowerPoint when his words buzz across her heart, sharp as a tattooist's needle. In the comfort break, she slips into a cubicle, thumbs up the message. His image streaks past, leaving her breathless. Face to the dryer, she blasts away her longing. Raises her eyebrows at a colleague, 'Meeting culture!', as they lean into the mirror, putting their faces to rights.

Later, she pours a glass of red, rustles up pasta with broccoli and anchovies while they chat. Enough for two. She'll pack the rest cold for the office tomorrow. 'Dangerous 'hood,' he crackles, flips so she can see the park squirrels sussing out a move on his bagel.

When he goes back to work, she takes a drive past his block. Each time, she has the dumb idea she might catch some glimpse of him, his hand pulling the front door to, his coattail flicking round the corner. The view never changes: the same parked cars under the same leafless trees, the pixellated stranger turning to stare.

Running her bath, she reads the menu from his local bar, chooses what he might buy her: salt beef and pickles, maybe, clam chowder.

When he comes home, she watches him shower, losing him in the steam, his singing ragged under the pounding water. As he dries, she carefully undresses for him. Behind her stands the wardrobe where his shirts – the ones that didn't make the cut – hang limp. He stretches back on the bed she has never slept in. On his bedside table, he keeps that photo of the beach, the wind tangling their hair together, someone's red kite hovering above them like a blessing. Some nights, she sees it's missing. Has he shoved it in a drawer, flattened it in haste, forgetting to turn it face-side up after some unseen late-night visitor has gone?

Their chat dwindles to a murmur, then a sigh. Their hands scroll down their silvered bodies; fingers pinch, drag and swipe. Afterwards, he tells her he loves her, waits for her to turn out the lamp before cutting the connection.

She pictures him then, standing, dressing, his evening just beginning. She tries to resist playing tag, searching for him at parties she hasn't been invited to given by people she has never met.

They say it's the blue light that stops you sleeping. Messes with the melatonin, like jet lag. That must be why she lies in the dark, open-eyed, wrapped in his frayed T-shirt, trying to remember the taste of his lips.

The Marriage of the Sea

They step on starburst, herringbone, chequerboard; each room, a different honeyed parquet floor. Glass chandeliers drop pulled-candy tentacles. The modern art baffles them, splodging the palazzo walls like the damp in their first, long-ago subterranean flat. But there's aircon and drawn blinds. When they emerge, blinking, into the light, the heat slaps.

The fish market slips with melting ice. The air smells liquid and salt. The stallholder slices them shrimp, a baby's thumb so fresh they eat it raw. Crabs wag wearied, pinioned claws. Fish glisten – silver, coral, blue – eyes at the very point of dimming.

Every year, for a thousand years, they read, the city has married the sea: rowers bend, fanfares blare, flags whip, a wedding band is cast like an anchor into the lagoon.

We wed thee, sea, as a sign of true and everlasting domination.

They lean on bridges, push tightening rings round hot, swollen fingers. They've billed it a second honeymoon. Both know it's a last chance.

They flee the crowds down passages that tang of piss and shit.

'That film, the little girl who drowned!'

They lose themselves in dead-end alleys, beneath listless washing.

'The red coat, the terrible killer!'

They find a green courtyard away from the furious sun. Only when they've finished their picnic, do they see the warnings for rat poison.

Their skin pinks and peels. They churn up and down the Grand Canal, the vaporetto gears grinding like a waking monster.

'Everything in this city is stolen.'

'Even the city is stolen from the sea.'

The promenade glitters sharp as knives. Tourists rustle, phones go up. The tug hauls in the giant liner, more spacecraft than cruise ship, its alien decks taller than the terracotta tiles and the bronze horses, stranger than the shining angels, than the winged lion itself.

They clasp masks to their faces and drink bittersweet Aperol Spritz. At midnight, with each strike of the great bell, the ground ripples under their feet.

They come apart in separate dreams. A chandelier blows out groping suckers. Thick water swallows a golden ring. The sea shakes off its domination and rises to reclaim its own.

Doin' What Comes Natur'lly

Bring in photos, they said. Of the old days.

Here's us in our heyday. The Swinging Sanders Sisters! Two hearts born to beat to one time! The lines the studio came up with. But it was true. Our bodies moved so perfectly together. Nothing else ever felt so complete.

Times change. Bodies thicken, and we fell out of fashion. We didn't mind; we had all those little hoofers to teach. Never married ourselves, we were dedicated to dance. People understood. So many lost sweethearts. Mine gone at El Alamein, we told them. Betty's at Dunkirk. Our secret heartache, the showbiz pages used to say.

A trouper to the end, Betty. Leading singsongs in the dayroom, 'Rum and Coca-Cola', 'Ac-Cent-Tchu-Ate the Positive'...

'Doin' What Comes Natur'lly'. That was her favourite. She'd sing those lines about how dumb folks are and hoot with laughter.

Some changes come too late. The day of the new law, I slipped the ring onto her finger. Our mother's, I told them. Which is half true. My mother left it to me. We're not sisters, of course. Another studio line. But it's served us well. They're nice people here, but we're a different generation. You can never be sure.

Musical memories are the last to go, they say. Every day, I sing to Betty. Once she stopped speaking, she'd sometimes sing along. Not now. But when I lay my finger on the soft skin of her wrist, I feel that rhythm still, two hearts, one time.

Her Safe Word is 'Circus'

But that's before trombone blares clarinet reedy squeaks bass drum thrums and clowns slick her lips oversize scarlet her nose glows holly berry and what's with her feet seee them streeeetch still everyone knows clowns are scary right so here's that word slipping through kiss-stopped smack by whiskery sea-lion bark the candystripe ball bouncing to and fro to and fro never dropping dipping into silver-slippery fish pail dipping for silver-glistening prize then whipcrack reels her back a necklace of teeth cradles her throat her head deep in a red raw meat furnace blazing and this must be it now must be no leopard-skin strongman diabolos her up on dappled appaloosa thumpety thump splayed arms she's tread tread treading thighs to that pounding rump round and round that very second as she's giddy-sliding her teeth bite, hard, and up she rises in glitterball twirl hanging on nothing but a smile while her toes find a line a fine one and sole by sole she chalks forward her body eeling this way that held up by held breath only and there it is the board she's going to make it don't look down the great O below her she looks down her arms wing back legs like clappers ringing a five-bell peal but firm fingers snatch her tipping ankles wrists spin her spirals loops somersaults 'til hands release a great gasp gusts from under and she's comet-tailing sequins falling no net falling yet here come the

clowns again sirenning in hosing glitter while wheels fall off
circling like a flower blooming and she lands on her back like
a starfish safe at last in the bull's-eye of the pulled white sheet.

The Mystery of Bay 53

You're clattering across the car park with the files from your two o'clock slithering under your frankly by now full-on sweating armpit, the phone on loudspeaker under your chin, letting Jasminder know you're going to be late for your four o'clock and can she call on because you'll be driving and, under your breath as the signal drops, if Jasminder could tell you where you parked the bloody car in the first place that would be just tremendous and while she's there can she please tell you what possessed you to buy a silver hatchback when the world is full of them each *exactly the same as the other,* and your fingers are clawing in your bag for the keys which are just as elusive as the bloody car but at least if you could reach them you might be able to get the damn thing to bip its dinky little lights for you when you almost step in it, and while some instinct makes you swerve a neat side-step, there go the papers all over the tarmac.

For fuck's sake, isn't there supposed to be a law about cleaning up your dog's mess these days?

You'll call her back, you tell Jasminder.

You squat, awkward muscles and joints complaining of too many hours behind the wheel and on metal-legged chairs in rooms darkened by vertical blinds. You reach gingerly for the nearest spreadsheet. At least nothing actually landed in it.

But it's not shit at all.

It is as plush and black as the inside of a jewellery box. Its pinhead eyes are as blind in death as they were in life. Its velvet coat ruffles in the slight breeze. Its great paws are lifted as if in prayer; its snout raised to follow some irresistible scent.

How did it end up here, everything concreted over for yards around?

You pick up a sales brochure, slide it gently under the tiny corpse. You hold it carefully in front of you like a ceremonial plate as you walk past bay after bay towards the thin line of cotoneaster and stunted mountain ash by the exit. With each step, you go back one year, two years, twenty or more into the field stretching down to the stream, and the tree pollen is tickling your nose, somewhere a blackbird is singing in the early morning light, and you're hunkering down like it's the easiest thing in the world watching the soil heave gently into soft mounds as if the earth itself is breathing.

How I Live Now the Demons Have Gone

When I was twelve, I took up with a poltergeist. We hurled chairs, slammed doors, smashed bottles to glitter, Catherine-wheeled to the ceiling. We chanted like harmonic toads. My parents called a priest who held me down with cold, carbolic hands.

Now I work in a tower of glass. The doors slide open without sound. I walk one inch above the ground in sensible heels. I recite long numbers with my heavy tongue. Occasionally, I bring home lovers. Over their shoulders, I watch the ceiling fan circle, round and round and round.

The Objects of My Affection

My husband, the wall

The breakfast sun melts over him like butter. I run my hands across his dips and hollows. No one else comes close like this – feels him soften in the slanting dawn, sees his stern facade pink and gild.

All day, my fingers dust my desk and keyboard with white-wash traces. My tongue flushes brick red with every call I take.

When I get home, the sun is setting. My ominous husband has hardened into shadow and blocks the falling light. I draw the blind and scrub my hands. I am sure, come morning, I will remember why I love him.

My wife, the clock

Her metal fingers push me on. Her routine strike defines my day. Her constant tap pursues me through each room. Tonck, tonck, tonck.

My steady wife requires I wind her once a week. I warm the key in my chafed hand. I wax her long case down. My dull reflection glances from its gleam.

Each spring, I steal an hour from her; she claims it back when autumn comes.

Some nights, I watch her movement click and whirr. Her brass teeth bite and cog my heart. In those small hours, I lie awake and strain to catch the hidden silence slipped between each beat.

My lover, the camera

They're the old-fashioned sort: turning me on with a thumb flick, rolling my secrets through their sealed belly, shielding me from the spoiling light.

Still, their focus takes me unawares. They lunge their sliding serpent lens, snap that shutter snick, zoom and shoot before I can prepare my smile.

While my perfidious lover sleeps, I reel away from their embrace. In the dark room's red ammoniac glow, I strip and bathe. Frame by frame, my negative self appears, hand raised, hair swinging, eyes averted from their harsh illuminating glare.

Rise

There was a time when I believed in dragons. I'd see the sunset scorch burnt orange and know the mark of a dragon's trail. Now the evening clouds hang heavy with grey as if they might rain ash. No apocalyptic downpour, just a dead drift groundward like the first woozy flakes of snow.

People say the green renews. I take myself instead to the sea for the swell, the dip and the hush, to taste the smack of salt.

You'd be surprised at what the tide throws up. The wrack lays down its twists of twine, sure, the misted bottle-traps, those cast-off claws that beckon nowhere. But the flotsam brings its puzzles too. I pick machine parts from the sidling foam, turn them in my hands, their purpose washed away in a wave-tumbled scouring. Yellow ducks, stranded on some lost migration, bob aimless round a rock pool. Once I found a box of doll's heads, glazed eyes staring or picked away. Perhaps the gulls had taken them. Keys glimmer in the shingle – Yale, Chubb, car. How do these people ever get home?

Twice each day, the sea closes, discloses, covers, discovers.

I comb the beach in the dawn light. The sand sucks at my feet, like a child's ice-cream kisses. The shale shelves bloom with ammonite curls. I trace trilobites scuttling for the overhang, arrowhead *Orthoceras* streaking through aeons. The weight of the world lies locked in these flat nabs.

One morning, above the high-tide line, I find at last the fragments I've been searching for: the talon's imprint, a tooth's sharp dent. I take my hammer, bit by bit begin to set them free. Each tap rings round the time-striped rock, strikes sparks, until the cliffs crack, crumble and, from the smoking rubble, I watch my dragons rise.

Ecdysis

The dragon darted from under Seth's sooty cuff. I flinched back, reached for a bottle to make it look as if I'd meant to make the move.

'What the hell made you choose that?' I said. 'Never seen one like it.'

In the candlelight, the creature shimmered, writhing round Seth's scrawny forearm as though it had taken whatever was left of his muscles for its own.

'Ah, here's the thing, see, doll.'

His voice crawled up through pits of tar.

'*You* don't choose. Tell him where ya want it. Get what you're given. What he—' he hooked yellow fingers '—"sees in you". Ain't she a beauty, though?'

It was beautiful, sure, but it made me sweat. I swear I could feel heat coming off it, smell smoke rising.

There was nobody in but Seth and the Peterson boys in the corner. I didn't want to know their business, and me and Seth got on well enough. But this was something else. He stretched for a candle, lit up his next stogie. The dragon flexed its wings.

'Hell's right though, doll.'

He leaned over his glass, nodding me in.

'Sold his soul, that's what they say.' He wiped his mouth with his hand, dragon jaws glinting. 'For his art, see. Worth it, d'ya think?'

The candles sputtered. Peterson's men, heading off to beat curfew. I went over to clear their empties, slam the door shut on the bitter wind.

'You'd best be moving too, Seth. Boss don't like you sleeping here after lights out. And keep things buttoned up, maybe?'

Seth knocked back his drink, pulled down his sleeve, damping the dragon's glow. As he stood, he flipped a card onto the bar.

'Get yourself something done, doll, why don't ya? S'only the next district. Don't charge nothing like you'd think. Get some damn colour in your life.'

~

Next day was our district's turn on the outage rota. Same old, same old. A week of indoor coats, cold food, candles all day – buttoned-up, flavourless, dim.

I tried to keep busy, but outage weeks were slow. People disappeared in the smogs. You didn't ask about them. I stopped in my room when I wasn't on shift.

I thought I'd thrown Seth's card away, but somehow it had gotten tucked over the register. Each time I rang in, there it was, address flickering in the candlelight like the letters were dancing.

~

When the power came back, I crossed to District 3. It wasn't an easy place to find. A slippery alley behind the ration store. I could hear something snuffling in the shadows, didn't want to see what it was.

There was no name, but the number was inked on the door, same twirling lettering as the card. I pressed the bell. The door buzzed open.

When I was little, my dad gave me a kaleidoscope. One of those mirrored tubes, you know? Twist it and tiny tiles inside rustle and slide into coloured patterns, like butterfly wings if you remember those. Never the same one twice. I lost it somewhere in the exodus. About the time I lost my dad.

Stepping into that room was like walking into my kaleidoscope. It was painted all over, the ceiling, even the floor. Hard to tell which way up you were standing. But these were pictures, not patterns. Men, tall, muscular, how I remember Dad, holding me high above his head. Animals with knowing eyes, creatures I couldn't name, fierce angels curving close wings round it all. I felt faint with a sugar-rush of colour. I had to drag my memory for the words: umber, ochre, emerald, magenta, vermilion, ultramarine. I said them out loud, needing to taste them on my tongue.

A figure peeled away from the wall.

'You come for a picture?'

'I don't have an appointment,' I said, heart jumping.

'Not necessary,' he said. 'You know how I work?'

'A friend told me.'

'So, you would like it where? Your picture?'

I hesitated. All through the outage, I had huddled in the dark, picturing those dragon colours, where on my body they might shine.

'Everywhere,' I said. 'I want to live in a different skin.'

He was silent for a minute. I thought he was going to refuse. Then he pointed to a screen. 'Undress.'

I shrugged out of my layers. It was a long time since anyone had seen me naked, but he wasn't looking at me like that. Still

I was ashamed of my body – blue-white and mottled like marble – in that jewel box of a room.

He told me to lie on the couch. A baby angel hovered above, finger to its lips. I held its painted eyes as he ran his hands over every inch of me. His touch was warm but rough, like a cat's tongue.

'I see it,' he said at last. 'Sleep, eat. If you are sure, come back next week.'

That night I dreamt in colour for the first time since I don't know when. A week later, I was back on the couch. This time the cat danced all over me, stippling my skin with tiny claws.

~

Seth died before I could thank him. Bed caught fire – one of those stinking stogies, so they say. He always said the smokes would get him in the end. I don't think he meant he'd actually burn, but after that dragon, well, it's no surprise to me.

I know the score now, see. I'm not afraid of anything anymore. I walk the dark streets anytime I choose. No one messes with me. Under my coat, leaves ripple with each stride; my arms branch open, my legs power, sturdy tree trunks. Across my back stands a russet-fleshed woman, apple in hand. The sweet juice oozes down my spine like a snake.

Zig Zag Girl

Each night, his saw bites through her. He locks her in boxes, stabs her with sabres, swivels her apart.

They call her the magician's girl, though her skin grids nowadays long after she has peeled her sticky fishnets away. She folds doves deep into pockets, beds rabbits in the hat's blackness. Her smile fixes while he takes the applause.

His whiskeyed hand nicks her bodice. 'Cut out the cake,' he growls when she shows him. She takes her finest needle, mends each satin tear with an invisible stitch.

The strong man offers a broad shoulder. She dries her eyes and drops her guard. This is the secret: the crowd mark the swirling cape, the masterful voice, and never think the skill is hers. How she flexes, squeezes, concertinas as they watch him carve her up.

'Feathers, legs, spangles. That's all they see.'

The strong man pats her arm, leans closer. His moustache pricks her cheek. Leopard skin crushes her thigh. His meat-stink breath all but overwhelms her before she wriggles free.

~

The miles spill out like knotted silk. Smokey compartments on panting trains. Never money for separate digs. She grips shuddering bedsteads until he's done. Pink-eyed rabbits blink through strands of rinsed stockings. The doves coo small comforts.

Her muscles wring from the ache of it, the bending and twisting. The endless smile.

~

They rehearse a new trick. Her suggestion. He shuts her up. The hidden trapdoor flaps; she vanishes! Then, at his word, restored, to the wonderment of all.

The curtain rises, the limelight flares. Ta-dah! His illusion shatters, misdirected. She has gone for sure. With the cashbox.

Scattered sequins sparkle straight along the pier. Too late, he hears the steamer's whistle blow, spies her standing tall on deck, doves streaming from her hands like a banner unfurling.

Harvest

Storms scour the dome like demons at a saint.

Inside, our weather is perfect. Algorithms set soft warmth and gentle showers to coax the hybrids from their calibrated beds.

Deep below, machines scrape the planet's mineral heart. The seedlings shiver. My instruments shake. I cannot tell if it is the ground's upward judder or my hand that tremors.

I lift my face to the recycled rain. Each drop has washed a thousand times through every body in the crew. My mouth opens to those rinsed memories, to reap the fleeting taste of flickering sunlight and wild greening on my tongue.

We're Hearing Reports of an Incident in Amsterdam

There's a weight to the petal, a rippled ice-cream thickness. Leaning as close as he dares, the wire scoring his ankles, he can follow the pressure guiding the brush, the swipe of the knife, that streak of bristle. It feels easy: turn his finger, track its worn, whorled pad along those inviting furrows. His hand strays instead over his beard. It's an illusion, he knows. Millions of dollars nest in those dabs and touches.

His eyes flick the label: *...blossom symbolising new life*. He steps back, for perspective. He can see the orchard now, the sinuous dance of branches, those delicate spatters of flowers. A dreamy couple, the woman's soft curve beginning to show, murmur their way along the wall then pause, heads together, obscuring his view. He closes his eyes and breathes, a lost honey scent, the remembered hum of bees, forgotten laughter. When he looks again, the couple has gone. A bell is ringing.

'Ladies and gentleman, the museum will be closing in ten minutes. Please start making your way to the exit.'

The attendant yawns and scratches his nose. A tour party in neon clatters across the next gallery.

Now is the time. A pulse beats in his temple.

Now.

He sways, as if about to fall, then he is pounding full force to the wall – and, yes, there are shouts and klaxons and flashing lights and an agony suspends him like a starburst in linseed and pigment and canvas threads but then the frame unfolds and he is through and the trees open their arms to receive him, scatter his head with confetti as he steps like a bride into the joyous peal of birdsong and the boundless spring.

Biodynamic

'Plant by the moon!' you urged us. 'She'll do the work.'

You marked up the calendar, the crescents of your nails eclipsed by their usual load of earth.

The chemical brigade grumbled; the rest of us smiled. Our resident hippy, off on one again. But that was before the growing season started.

'Beans should be planted on a fire day,' you said, leading us through rows thrumming like power stations with bees. 'An earth day,' you said, brushing away cake-crumbs of soil, 'that's the time to pull carrots.' Their crunch was almost as sweet as your strawberries. (You left most of those for the blackbirds.) You heaped our arms with cabbages, each as big as a toddler's head. At dusk, pumpkins glowed across your patch like harvest suns.

You took home best in show. We swotted-up on lunar cycles.

You laughed when you began to bleed again. 'Thought the moon was done with an old girl like me!'

It took three of us, round the Kelly kettle, mugs of strong tea, a tin of your honey flapjack, to persuade you to make the appointment.

Holding the scan to the light, they revealed that dark, unwelcome seed germinating deep inside you.

You never had time for husband, children. 'Too much world to see!' So we took turns driving you to hospital, sitting with you. 'My allotment family,' you called us, winding scarves bright as autumn leaves round your scalp. You pored over catalogues in those long waiting-room days. Two ticks for old favourites, a question mark for new varieties you were keen to try. 'Might get you to start these off for me,' you said. 'Remember, it's a water day for lettuces.'

You never said, but you'd bought your own plot years before. We should have guessed you'd choose rich loam over fire and ash. We buried you on an air day, lit by the winter sun. Two days before new moon. A good time for planting. You'd have liked that.

Not Love Which Alters Where It Alteration Finds

I find you in the forest at first light, your skin pale as moonshine. I swaddle you in wool. The farm dogs bay as we drive home. No birds sing.

I wipe the red from your mouth and spoon you warm milk. You whimper and kick like a puppy dreaming. I press my lips to your rough hair. It tastes like pine, detergent. I leave the curtains open to the sun.

When you stagger down, I mash bananas into yoghurt in your favourite bowl.

'I could murder a steak.' Your grin is yellow and ragged.

We do the crossword, listen to the news. We do not say, it's getting worse; we do not say, each time cuts deeper.

You rally enough to walk across the bridge. We drop sticks into the water.

'Never the same river twice.'

We have thrown out the calendars, but the days pull through us like the tides. I know when it begins. Your fingers claw and rap, you snap at small talk. Your gaze turns to the window and the moor.

I did watch, once, though you forbid it. Sometimes, while you sleep, I crouch, I stretch, I bare my teeth, I howl. My stubborn skin stays smooth and soft. Beloved, forgive me. I cannot share this fearful transformation.

I think you hate me for it. Your smouldering eye warns you would devour me if you could. But I will stay until the silver bullet takes you, until the day this curse will pass to me.

The Perfectionist Struggles with Grief

1.

It slips from your hand, a sly fish-leap you cannot grasp, and chunks on the tiles.

The crash rattles the silent house.

You had carried it home, swaddled in that jumper you'd packed *just in case* but never needed in that cricket-chirping heat. All these years it has held fruit and holiday and sunshine and promise and what it meant to be smooth-limbed and sure-footed and young.

Stark white scars the lavender blue. When you run your thumb along an edge, a thread of blood rises on the unexpected rawness.

2.

You scrutinise YouTube for hours, then head to the hardware store. The metal aisles tower over you like prison fences.

You spread paper over the table and lay out what you need: brushes of varying thickness, the broken pieces, liquid gold, a chubby tube of glue.

It is the perfect opportunity. A lucky accident. The breaks are clean. You've been dying to try this. *Kintsugi* – to mend with gold, leaving the broken more beautiful than before.

You will make this whole again.

Your hand is steady as you gild the seams. Not too much glue or it will be lumpy. Your tongue pinks out like a child's.

You replace the bowl, heap it with clementines, their beacon glow and pert green stalks. Good as new. Better.

3.

The nights chill. You set a match to the long-laid fire, but the wood has slumped damp from sitting. You hold a sheet of newspaper to the firebox. Through the rising yellow, you read disasters, scandals, downturns. The suck and pull flames to a whistling roar.

You sit back, take an orange from the bowl, peel it with care. Still the essence of it spurts up, spits tears into your eye. You blink back hard. You try not to notice how, in the flickering light, the gold of your mending streaks like rust on a derelict hull.

A Seven-Step Recovery Programme Following Loss

1.

Women come with cake. She measures their concern by the size of slice they cut themselves, the acuteness of their angle as they lean forward, stirring. When they leave, she seals the cake in airtight tins.

2.

The house fills with absence like a slow-run bath. The laundry basket half empty, the coat hook protruding like an unset bone, the hollow down one side of the bed.

The TV screen stares back at her.

The cat's claws prick through her jeans. Her gaze switches to the amber quiz of its eyes.

3.

She finds gifts in unexpected places. A shred of grey silk in the bathroom, a delicate fan splayed on the rug. There is a language of fans, she recalls from some talk. She cannot decipher this one.

Disposing of bodies was her husband's job, hard-bargained when she had pleaded dog, and he'd insisted cat. She gloves her hands like a murderer, bags up the baby pigeon under the washbasin, the sparrow's wing by the hearth. Thinks, perhaps a puppy.

4.

She believes she does not sleep but wakes dry-eyed in the dark. The cat's heavy warmth has her feet pinned down.

5.

The women no longer come.

She opens tins, discovers ossified cake. She scatters crumbs for the birds.

In the small hours, she hears the cat singing. Next morning, the kitchen floor is feathered white. It is like walking across an angel's wing.

6.

A dark jewel gleams by her shoes. It charms her.

It is a jet-black mouse nose. Just the nose, and whiskers.

She sleeps, mostly, in the daytime, now.

7.

They slip from the house once the moon is high. The cat pads in front, does not look back. She follows it into the night, her pupils black and deep as wells.

A Household Guide to Mourning Etiquette for Widows

Funeral

Hill's fingers tap her spine like a ghost at the window. She shivers. No one touches her now but the maid and the baby, tugging at her breast. No hand traces the round of her stomach, the curve of her hip.

Hill tightens the laces. Her ribs curl, her heart displaces, her breath shallows. It feels like an embrace. If there is nothing to hold her in, she will fall apart.

The dress blots the floor, a black pool. She steps in, raises her arms like a drowning woman dragged down by weeds as Hill lifts the stiff bombazine about her.

At the front door, she drops the veil. The world darkens as if it is she who is lowered into the grave.

Full mourning – to be worn for one year

She may neither visit nor receive visitors. She circles the garden, while Hill walks out with the baby. Her sheenless skirts deaden the winter light. Seed heads hang in the frost. When she tries the side door to the orchard, she finds it locked.

Each night, she staggers as Hill unhooks the whalebone stays.

On honeymoon, unlacing her, he had whispered how the great whales sang in the southern seas. Such swooning, such swooping could only be the call of love across the deep.

She rolls to the cold side of the bed, his side. Her hand falls to the ache between her thighs, but she hears only the whistle of her own thinned blood.

Second mourning – to be worn for nine months

Hill unpicks the crepe ribbons from her dress. The baby, crawling now, sucks a strand to softness like kelp.

Certain jewellery becomes permissible. She pins jet to her throat. As she enters church black-bead eyes speculate her worth, calculate how long before she becomes available.

She takes down the drapes covering the mirrors, yearning to find him trapped within the dimpled glass. Her face alone stares back, unfamiliar. Empty rooms unfold behind her.

Half mourning – to be worn for three months

She sits by the fire in her ash-grey dress, reading to her shadow husband in his vacant chair. She can no longer summon the pitch of his voice. In the hallway, Hill shushes the child's staggering giggle.

Out

The boy – no longer a baby – runs ahead and waits by the orchard door. The breeze ruffles his dandelion hair. His face is opening like a rose, his father's eyes, that tilt of his chin.

Hill hands her the heavy key. It snubs in the lock. She works it into place, gives a firm twist, presses her hand to the creaking wood. The boy, copying, leans and adds his newfound weight to hers. The door gives. She gathers her forget-me-not skirts and takes his sticky hand. Together they step through the opening into the blossoming, snow-white spring.

My Father Comforts Me in the Form of Birds

Heron

The December tarmac's glazing treacherous black. My mind should be on the road, not with my mother, left in the echoing house.

I take the roundabout too fast.

There it is, standing guard. I've never seen one here. No water, only frozen fields. Sentinel grey, crunched into its awkward bones, those quilling eyebrows. Unmistakable.

I hear his voice.

'Hamba gashle.'

'What's that, Dad?'

'It's Zulu. It means...'

I whisper it back as the light fades.

'...Go safely.'

I flip the visor against the falling sun.

Pheasant

We startle them into clattering flight. Survivors, seeing the New Year in against the odds.

One stays grounded, escorts us like a maverick sheepdog hitching a walk.

That look. *'Dad?'* Joking.

It stops. Its feathers glint rainbows in the iced light.
That sideways look. *'Is that you, Dad?'* Half-joking.
The absurd lens of grief.

Sparrowhawk?

Hard to tell. We pass so quickly.
Roadside perch. Sharp eyes scanning.
'What do I always say?'
'Keep your options open, Dad.'

Robin

On a clear day, you can see the hills he loved from here.
This is not a clear day.
Every voice feels winter-stopped.
In the branches, a spot of red, defiant.
'The robin keeps singing right through the winter.'
Its sweet strain clarifies the clouded air.
'Very few birds do that, you know.'
The mist begins to lift, a little.

Goldfinch

The feeders have swung empty for months. We knock the nails in lower so Mum can reach, refill them with rich sunflower hearts.

'They're back!'

From the kitchen window, we watch a charm of gold glitter the garden.

Curlew

Spring loops in on that cool, clear call, back to breed on the hard, high moors.

'That day we found a nest, remember? The baby curlew? The parent bird circling overhead?'

The wind lifts heady scent from the greening woods, scatters blossom like confetti, accepts the ash we offer.

Skylark

You hear it first, notes like diamonds etching glass.

Lift your head. Turn your face to the full sun.

'Look long enough, you will see it.'

There, infinitesimal in the infinite blue.

Do you see him?

Yes! There! Rising, singing, rising...

ACKNOWLEDGEMENTS

The flash fiction community is an endlessly supportive one, with so much cheerleading for each other and so many people working so hard to publish and share this wonderful form for the sheer love of it. You all make writing and reading flash fiction a joy. These stories wouldn't exist without you.

I'd like to thank in particular: Jude Higgins and everyone behind the scenes at Ad Hoc Fiction, Bath Flash Fiction Award and the UK Flash Fiction Festival; David Borrowdale and Reflex Press for having faith in this collection; my *FlashBack Fiction* family, for their editorial wisdom and comradeship; Kirsty Logan and Jenn Ashworth, who I've been lucky enough to have as generous mentors; New Writing North and The Word Factory, for their invaluable and extensive support; Kathy Fish, flash writer and teacher extraordinaire, in whose workshops many of these pieces were born and where I've met so many inspiring writers; Michelle Elvy, for picking my stories for life-changing prizes, not once but twice; all the readers and editors who have selected my pieces for publication and – as importantly – rejected them when they weren't ready; and Peter, for belief, confidence-boosting and some crucial first readings.

~

The author and publisher wish to thank the editors of the publications in which the following stories first appeared, online or in print:

'Telegraph' was first published by *Ad Hoc Fiction*, April 2016; 'First Catch Your Hare' – *To Carry Her Home* (Bath Flash Fiction Award anthology), December 2016; 'A Jolly Good Fellow' – *Faber Academy QuickFic*, July 2015; 'Terra Incognita' – *To Carry Her Home* (Bath Flash Fiction Award anthology), December 2016; 'Undelivered' – *Ad Hoc Fiction*, October 2015; 'Gelsenkirchen: 10/10ths Cloud, Thirty Aircraft Lost' – *Splonk Issue 3*, June 2020; 'How I Became a Star' – *The Cabinet of Heed Issue 3*, January 2018; 'Nomad' – *Stories for Homes Volume 2*, October 2017; 'Them Flowers in the Dark' – *Ellipsis Zine Three*, 2018; 'Mr Punch in Love' – *Riggwelter Issue 3*, November 2017; 'Down the Rabbit Hole' – *Faber Academy QuickFic*, August 2015; 'If We Could Knock Through' – *TSS Publishing*, August 2017; 'There Was No Possibility of Taking a Walk That Day' – *Faber Academy QuickFic*, January 2015; 'The Firestarters' – (as 'Swarm') *Halo Magazine*, 2017; 'The Sweetest Poison Kills You Slowest' – *Reflex Fiction*, September 2017; 'Picnic at the End of the World' – *The Cabinet of Heed Issue 17*, February 2019; 'Even to the Edge of Doom' – *Flash Frontier*, September 2019; 'Caramel Baby' – *Ripening* (National Flash Fiction Day anthology), June 2018; 'Renovation' – *Faber Academy QuickFic*, February 2015; 'Health and Pleasure, Glorious Sea!' – *A Box of Stars Beneath the Bed* (National Flash Fiction Day anthology), June 2016; 'Rockpooling' – *Faber Academy QuickFic*, April 2016; 'Sea Change' – *Hysteria 5*, November 2016; 'Downhill' – *Cambridge Fiction Award*, July 2015; 'Walking on Eggshells' – *TSS Publishing*, April 2020; 'Motel Road Trip Honeymoon Postcards' – *To Carry Her Home* (Bath Flash Fiction Award anthology), December 2016; 'Modern Love' – (as 'Never Going to Fall for Modern Love') *Sleep is A Beautiful Colour* (National Flash Fiction Day anthology), June 2017; 'The Marriage of the Sea' – *Reflex Fiction*, June 2020; 'Her Safe Word is 'Circus'' – *With One Eye on the Cows* (Bath Flash Fiction Award anthology), December 2019; 'The Mystery of Bay 53' – *National Flash Fiction Day 'Flash Flood'*, June 2019; 'How I Live Now the Demons Have Gone' – *National Flash Fiction Day NZ, Flash Frontier*, June 2018; 'The Objects of My Affection' – *New Flash Fiction Review*, March 2019; 'Zig Zag Girl' – *Things Left and Found by the Side of the Road* (Bath Flash Fiction Award anthology), December 2018; 'Harvest' – *Ellipsis Zine, Six: 2119*, October 2019; 'We're Hearing Reports of an Incident in Amsterdam' – *Spelk*, February 2019; 'Biodynamic' – *Spelk*, July 2017; 'A Seven-Step Recovery Programme Following Loss' – *The Lobsters Run Free* (Bath Flash Fiction Award anthology), December 2017; 'A Household Guide to Mourning Etiquette for Widows' – *Splonk*, May 2019; 'My Father Comforts Me in the Form of Birds' – *Reflex Fiction*, June 2018.

REFLEX PRESS

Reflex Press is an independent publisher based in Abingdon, Oxfordshire, committed to publishing bold and innovative books by emerging authors from across the UK and beyond.

Since our inception in 2018, we have published award-winning short story collections, flash fiction anthologies, and novella-length fiction.

www.reflex.press
@reflexfiction